£1.75

Oxford Junior English 1
Oliver Gregory

Illustrated by
Kathy Wyatt
Martin White

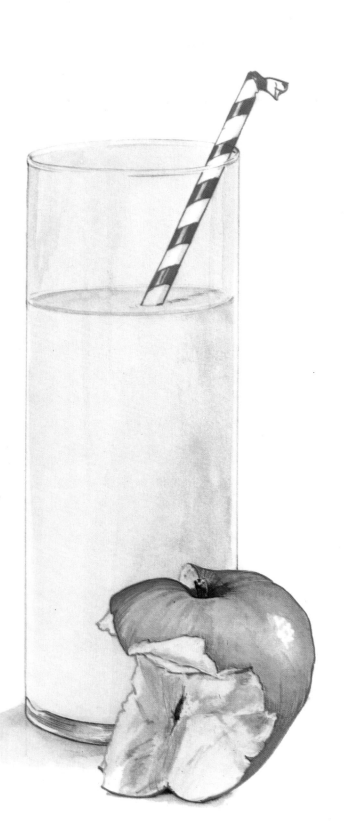

Oxford University Press

1   Sara

2   Paul

3   Mark

4   Julie

5   Kay

6   George

Who are they?

Look at the pictures.
Look at the sentences in the box.
Write the sentences in the same order as the pictures.
Number your sentences 1 to 6.

> This is Julie.
> This is Mark.
> This is Paul.
> This is George.
> This is Sara.
> This is Kay.

What have they got?

Look at the pictures.
Look at the sentences in the box.
Write the sentences in the same order as the pictures.
Number your sentences 1 to 6.

> Kay has a kite.
> George has a football.
> Julie has a swing.
> Sara has a bicycle.
> Mark has a comic.
> Paul has a gun.

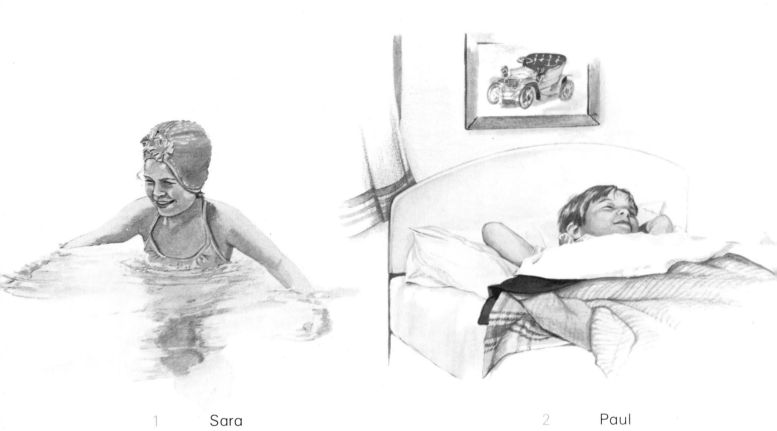

1   Sara

2   Paul

3   Mark

4   Julie

4

5   Kay

6   George

What are they doing?

Look at the pictures.
Look at the sentences in the box.
Write the sentences in the same order as the pictures.
Number your sentences 1 to 6.

> Mark is fishing.
> Kay is digging.
> Sara is swimming.
> George is eating.
> Paul is sleeping.
> Julie is skipping.

Where are they?

Look at the pictures.
Look at the sentences in the box.
Write the sentences in the same order as the pictures.
Number your sentences 1 to 6.

> Kay is in the garden.
> Julie is in the playground.
> Sara is in the water.
> Paul is in the bedroom.
> George is at the table.
> Mark is by the river.

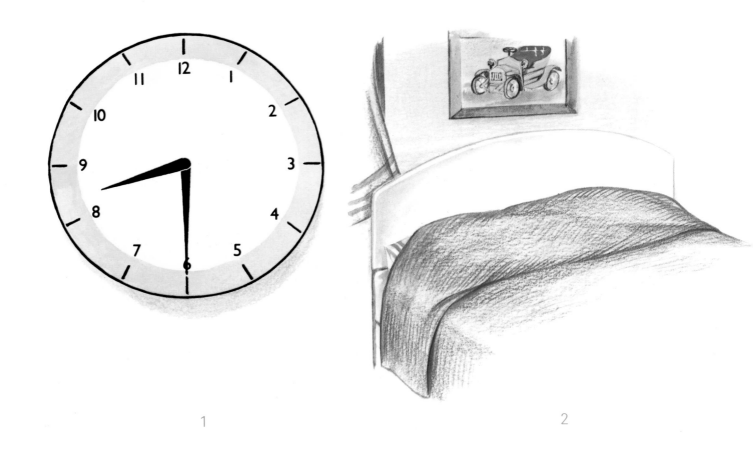

1

2

3

4

5

6

What are they?

Look at the pictures.
Look at the sentences in the box.
Write the sentences in the same order as the pictures.
Number your sentences 1 to 6.

> This is a tree.
> This is a table.
> This is a jug.
> This is a clock.
> This is a bed.
> This is a desk.

Where are they?

Look at the pictures.
Look at the sentences in the box.
Write the sentences in the same order as the pictures.
Number your sentences 1 to 6.

> The bed is in the bedroom.
> The tree is in the park.
> The desk is in the classroom.
> The clock is on the wall.
> The table is in the kitchen.
> The jug is on the table.

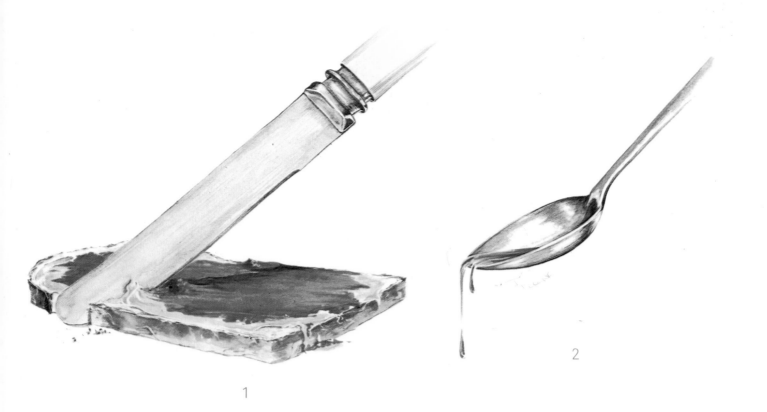

1

2

3

4

5

6

What are they?

Look at the pictures.
Look at the sentences in the box.
Write the sentences in the same order as the pictures.
Number your sentences 1 to 6.

This is a spoon.
This is a brush.
This is a ruler.
This is a knife.
This is a spade.
This is a pencil.

What do we do with them?

Look at the pictures.
Look at the sentences in the box.
Write the sentences in the same order as the pictures.
Number your sentences 1 to 6.

We write with a pencil.
We paint with a brush.
We cut with a knife.
We dig with a spade.
We eat with a spoon.
We measure with a ruler.

Breakfast time

It is half past eight.

Sara and Mum are in the kitchen.

Sara is eating cornflakes.

Mum is drinking tea.

"What's happened to Paul?" asks Sara.

"Late as usual," says Mum.

a Write a sentence for each answer.

1 What time is it?
2 Where are Sara and Mum?
3 What is Sara doing?
4 What is Mum doing?
5 Who is late for breakfast?

b These sentences have got mixed up.
    Put the right parts together.

1 The food is   facing each other.
2 Sara and Mum sit   on the right.
3 Sara sits   on the wall.
4 Mum sits   on the table.
5 The clock is   on the left.

c Here are the names of some things on
    the table. Write the names of the things
    we can eat or drink.

    jug   bread   spoon   butter   knife
    milk   plate   sugar   cup   cornflakes

d Write the five sentences that are true.

1 Sara and Mum are in the bathroom.
    Sara and Mum are in the kitchen.
2 Sara and Mum are sitting at the table.
    Sara and Mum are sitting on the floor.
3 Sara is holding a spoon.
    Sara is holding a knife.
4 There are three chairs in the picture.
    There are two chairs in the picture.
5 It is half past eight in the evening.
    It is half past eight in the morning.

e Notice that each sentence should begin
    with a capital letter and end with a full
    stop. Write these out correctly.

1 the food is on the table
2 it is breakfast time
3 soon it will be time to go to school

11

Going to school

Sara and Paul are going to school.

They meet Mark and Julie at the corner.

On the way they see two buses,
three vans and seven cars.

They cross the road carefully.

It takes ten minutes to get to school.

When the children get to school
they wait in the playground.

a Write a sentence for each answer.

1 Where are Sara and Paul going?
2 How many buses do they see?
3 How many vans do they see?
4 How many cars do they see?
5 How long does it take to get to school?

b Here are some words that tell what the children do.

see   wait   meet   cross   walk

Write the sentences, filling each blank with one of these words.

1 Sara and Paul_____to school.
2 They_____cars on the road.
3 They_____Mark and Julie.
4 The children_____the road carefully.
5 They_____in the playground.

c Here are some sentences about what Sara and Paul did.
Write them out in the proper order.

When they got to school they waited in the playground.

Sara and Paul had their breakfast.

On the way they met Julie and Mark.

After breakfast they set out for school.

d Write the five sentences that are true.

1 The children are going to school.
The children are going to bed.
2 They meet their friends on the bus.
They meet their friends at the corner.
3 They see cows on the road.
They see traffic on the road.

4 It doesn't take long to get to school.
It takes a long time to get to school.
5 At school they wait inside.
At school they wait outside.

e Put the right words together to make longer words. (All the longer words have been used in this book so far.)

foot   fast
break   flakes
bed   ball
corn   ground
play   room

OFFICIAL

13

In the playground

The children are in the playground.

Sara is eating an apple.

Paul is eating crisps.

Mark is kicking a ball.

Julie and Kay are running across the playground.

George is standing by the gate.

a Write a sentence for each answer.

1 Where are the children?
2 What is Sara doing?
3 What is Paul doing?
4 What is Mark doing?
5 What are Julie and Kay doing?

b Is, are
Notice that we say George is standing. Julie and Kay are running.

Write the sentences, filling each blank with is **or** are.

1 The children_____at school.
2 Sara_____holding an apple.
3 George_____near the gate.
4 Two girls_____running across the playground.
5 Some of the boys_____playing football.

c A, an
Notice that we say a ball **but** an apple.

Write these, filling each blank with a **or** an.

_____ orange   _____ cake
_____ bus   _____ uncle
_____ car   _____ horse
_____ apple   _____ elephant
_____ dog   _____ island

d Write the five sentences that are true.

1 The children are inside.
  The children are outside.
2 It is daytime.
  It is night-time.
3 Sara has a banana.
  Sara has an apple.

4 Mark catches the ball.
  Mark kicks the ball.
5 George is not running.
  George is running.

e | coat   milk   cake   bicycle   book |

1 Which one would you eat?
2 Which one would you read?
3 Which one would you wear?
4 Which one would you ride?
5 Which one would you drink?

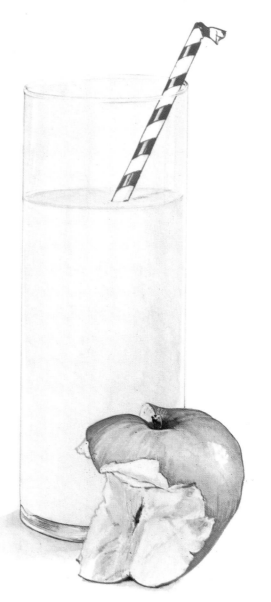

In the classroom

The children are in the classroom.

Sara sits next to Julie.

George sits next to Andy.

The girls are writing stories.

George reads his book.

Andy is drawing a picture.

a Write a sentence for each answer.

1 Where are the children?
2 Who sits next to Julie?
3 Who sits next to Andy?
4 What are the girls doing?
5 Who is drawing a picture?

b Is, his
Notice that we say
George reads his book.
The word his **means that the book belongs to him.**

Write the sentences, filling each blank with is **or** his.

1 The boy reads_____book.
2 The desk_____in the classroom.
3 Andy has finished_____writing.
4 Now he_____drawing a picture.
5 Paul goes to school with_____sister.

c Write the sentences that tell about the things we do in the classroom.

We read books.   We ride horses.
We climb trees.   We dig holes.
We draw pictures.   We write stories.
We ride bicycles.   We watch television.
We sing songs.   We catch fish.

d Write the five sentences that are true.

1 The children are in school.
  The children are in bed.
2 Julie sits next to Paul.
  Julie sits next to Sara.
3 Andy and George sit next to each other.
  Andy and George do not sit next to each other.
4 George is painting.
  George is reading.
5 One of the boys is drawing a picture.
  One of the girls is drawing a picture.

e Notice that the names of the children have capital letters.
Write the sentences, putting in capital letters and full stops in the right places

1 the boys and girls are in school
2 andy sits next to george
3 the children are working hard
4 sara and julie are writing

17

A story

The teacher is reading a story to the class.
It is called The Gentle Tiger.
It is a story about a tiger
who lived in a forest.
He wanted to be kind and gentle
and make friends with people.
All the other tigers in the forest
wanted to be fierce.
They left the gentle tiger
to go his own way.

a Write a sentence for each answer.

1 Who is reading the story?
2 What is the story called?
3 Where did the tiger live?
4 What did the tiger want?
5 What did the other tigers want?

b Notice that we say one tiger **but** two tigers.

Now write out and finish these.

1 We say one book but two _____ .
2 We say one girl but two _____ .
3 We say one song but two _____ .
4 We say one boy but two _____ .
5 We say one car but two _____ .

c Write these sentences, filling each blank with a word taken from those in the box.

shell	neck	hump	stripes
	scales	trunk	

1 A tiger has _____ .
2 A giraffe has a long _____ .
3 An elephant has a _____
4 A camel has a _____ .
5 A tortoise has a _____ .
6 Most fish have _____ .

d Write the five sentences that are true.

1 The teacher is reading a story.
 Julie is reading a story.

2 The teacher is reading to herself.
 The teacher is reading to the class.

3 The story is about a lion.
 The story is about a tiger.

4 All the tigers wanted to be friendly with people.
 One tiger wanted to be friendly with people.

5 The gentle tiger was left on his own.
 The gentle tiger went with the other tigers.

e Can you think of a way to tell the rest of the story? Perhaps you could think of how the gentle tiger could show people that he wanted only to be friendly. Perhaps you could think of how he could help someone so that they might begin to trust him. Don't forget to say what the other tigers might think of all this.

Dinner time

It is half past twelve.

The children are in the school hall
    having their dinner.

It is very noisy in the hall.

Paul and Mark sit with Kay and Lyn.

They are eating meat, potatoes and carrots.

After dinner the children play outside.

George and Andy are not at school.

They go home for their dinner.

a Write a sentence for each answer.

1 What time is it?
2 Which boys sit with Kay and Lyn?
3 What are the children eating?
4 What do the children do after dinner?
5 Where do George and Andy go for their dinner?

b Notice **how we use** there **and** their.

Their **always means belonging to someone.**

Write the sentences, filling each blank with there **or** their.

1 The children are eating_____dinner.
2 Sara and Julie are sitting over_____ .
3 If_____is time the children will play.
4 George and Andy have dinner with _____parents.
5 They will return to_____class after dinner.

c In each line find one word that is different.

1 apple   lemon   jam   plum
2 dinner   supper   picnic breakfast
3 fruit   bread   cake   bun
4 milk   butter   coffee lemonade

d Write the five sentences that are true.

1 It is half past two.
  It is half past twelve.
2 Some of the children are on the roof.
  Some of the children are in school.
3 It is dinner time.
  It is supper time.
4 It is noisy in the hall.
  It is quiet in the hall.
5 All children stay at school at dinner time.
  Some children go home at dinner time.

e Here are some mixed-up pairs of things that often go together.
Write them out, putting the right parts together.

fish	and	butter
knife	and	pepper
cup	and	chips
salt	and	fork
bread	and	saucer

21

Things to do at home

It is seven o'clock in the evening.

Sara and Paul are at home with their parents.

There is a table by the wall
   and there are two chairs at the table.

Sara and Paul sit at the table.

Sara is cutting out pictures
   while Paul writes in his book.

Mum is watching television
   but Dad has fallen asleep.

a Write a sentence for each answer.

1 Where are Sara and Paul?
2 Where is the table?
3 Who is cutting out pictures?
4 What is Paul doing?
5 Who has fallen asleep?

b There is, there are

Notice that we say
There is a table.
There are two chairs.
Write the sentences, filling each blank with either
There is **or** There are

1 _____ a table in the room.
2 _____ two big chairs in the room.
3 _____ four people in the room.
4 _____ a carpet on the floor.
5 _____ two children at the table.

c Paul has been writing some puzzles. Try to work them out.
Begin each answer with the words
I am a _____

Choose the endings from words in the box.

clock river comb
table potato

1 I have legs but cannot walk.
2 I have hands but cannot hold things.
3 I have teeth but cannot bite.
4 I have eyes but cannot see.
5 I have a mouth but cannot eat.

d Write the sentences about Sara and Paul at home. Choose the right endings from the words in brackets.

1 It is seven o'clock in the (morning, evening).
2 There is a table by the (wall, ceiling).
3 Sara and Paul are (dancing, sitting).
4 Sara is holding a pair of (shoes, scissors).
5 Paul is using a (pencil, potato).

e Sara is cutting out pictures of things that we wear. Choose from this list the things that she is looking for.

car	dress
shoes	sheet
coat	trousers
plate	table
carpet	shirt

People at work

Julie's father is a policeman.
He drives a police car.
Julie's mother is a typist.
She works in an office.
Kay's mother works in a shop.
Lyn's father is a painter.
George's father is a bus driver.
Andy's father is a doctor.

a Write a sentence for each answer.

1 What does Julie's father drive?
2 Where does Julie's mother work?
3 Who works in a shop?
4 What does George's father drive?
5 Who is a painter?

b These sentences tell about the work that people do, but the parts have got mixed up. Write them out, putting the right parts together.

1 Fishermen   look after people who are ill.
2 Miners   look after our teeth.
3 Nurses   paint pictures.
4 Dentists   catch fish.
5 Artists   dig for coal.

c These sentences tell us about the things that people use in their work, but the parts have got mixed up. Write them out, putting the right parts together.

1 A typist uses   a plough.
2 A painter uses   a hose pipe.
3 A farmer uses   a typewriter.
4 A baker uses   bricks.
5 A fireman uses   scissors.
6 A hairdresser uses   a paint brush.
7 A bricklayer uses   flour.

d Here is another puzzle to work out. Can you put the names of the people with the work they do. Begin like this:

1 Mr Rider is a jockey.

1 Mr Rider is   a farmer.
2 Mr Flowers is   a bank manager.
3 Mr Field is   a fireman.
4 Mr Lamb is   a postman.
5 Mr Burns is   a jockey.
6 Mr Wall is   a shepherd.
7 Mr Stamp is   a gardener.
8 Mr Pound is   a builder.

e Copy out from this list all the things that Julie's mother would use in her work.

spade   paper
rubber   hammer
spoon   typewriter
tractor   envelopes
pen   net

In the park

On Saturday Sara and Paul went to the park.

They saw two boys playing football
   and two girls playing tennis.

They saw two ponds in the park.

Some children were paddling in the first pond.

Two ducks were on the second pond.

"Look," said Paul. "There's a lady throwing
   crumbs to the ducks."

"Yes," said Sara. "If you're a good boy
   perhaps she'll give you some."

a Write a sentence for each answer.

1 When did Sara and Paul go to the park?
2 What were the two boys playing?
3 What were the two girls playing?
4 Where were the children paddling?
5 Where were the ducks?

b To, two

Remember that two always means the number 2.
Write the sentences, filling each blank with to or two.

1 The children went_____the park.
2 There were_____boys playing football.
3 The lady threw crumbs_____the ducks.
4 The_____ducks ate the crumbs.
5 At last it was time_____go home.

c Here are some sentences that tell what it is like in the park in summer and in winter. Write the words In Summer and write the sentences that belong to summer. Then write In Winter and write the sentences that belong to winter.

It is very cold.
It is very warm.
The trees are bare.
There are leaves on the trees.
The pond is frozen.
Children are paddling in the pond.
Some people are sunbathing.
There is snow on the ground.
People are wearing coats and scarves.
There are lots of flowers in bloom.

d Here are some more sentences about things we can do in the park.
Write them out, putting the right parts together.

1 We fly   a ball.
2 We kick   a game.
3 We climb   a boat.
4 We sail   a kite.
5 We play   a tree.

e Copy out from this list all the things that you think Sara and Paul saw in the park.

trees   lighthouse
sharks   water
birds   factory
lifeboat   flowers
grass   carpet

The supermarket

While Sara and Paul are in the park
Mum and Dad go to the supermarket.

They go to buy things to eat.

Dad pushes a trolley as they walk round.

Mum and Dad take the things they want
and put them in the trolley.

They wanted some bread as well,
but there is none left.

As soon as they have finished
they pay the girl at the desk.

Mum has the money in her purse.

a Write a sentence for each answer.

1 Where are Sara and Paul?
2 Where do Mum and Dad go?
3 Why do they go to the supermarket?
4 Who pushes a trolley?
5 Who has the money?

b As, has

Write the sentences, filling each blank with as or has.

1 Mum_____a purse.
2 Dad_____the trolley.
3 They walk round_____quickly_____ they can.
4 The supermarket_____run out of bread.
5 Mum and Dad pay the girl_____soon _____they have finished.

c And, but

Notice how we use these words. We can say
The door was locked but I had a key.
The door was locked and I could not open it.

Now write these sentences, filling each blank with and or but.

1 Mum and Dad go shopping_____the children would rather go to the park.
2 The shop is busy_____it takes time to get round.
3 They look for some bread_____cannot find any.
4 Mum opens her purse_____takes out the money.
5 They finish their shopping_____go back home.

d Write the sentences that are true.

1 Sara and Paul are with their parents.
Sara and Paul are not with their parents.
2 Mum and Dad are in the garden.
Mum and Dad have gone shopping.
3 Dad pushes a trolley.
Dad pushes a pram.
4 The money is in Mum's purse.
The money is in Mum's hat.
5 The girl sits on the floor.
The girl sits at the desk.

e Write True or Not true for each of these sentences.

1 Bread is made from flour.
2 Carrots grow on trees.
3 Jam is made from fruit.
4 Peas grow in tins.
5 Meat comes from animals.

29

At the zoo

SQUIRREL MONKEY

During the holidays Sara and Paul
   went to the zoo.

There were lots of animals to see.

First of all they saw some monkeys.

The monkeys were in a cage.

Then they went to the reptile house
   where they saw some snakes.

In another part of the zoo they saw
   a young giraffe with its mother.

a Write a sentence for each answer.

1 When did Sara and Paul go to the zoo?
2 Which animals did they see first?
3 Where were the monkeys?
4 What did they see in the reptile house?
5 What did they see in another part of the zoo?

b Where and were

Remember that where **refers to a place.**
Write the sentences, filling each blank
with where **or** were.

1 Sara and Paul_____on holiday.
2 A zoo is a place_____animals are kept.
3 There_____many animals at the zoo.
4 The giraffes_____standing side by side.
5 Later, the children went to the aviary_____they saw some birds.

c Here are the names of some animals and the noises they make.
Write them out, putting the right parts together.

1	Monkeys	hiss
2	Snakes	bark
3	Cats	roar
4	Dogs	chatter
5	Lions	bray
6	Donkeys	purr
7	Horses	cluck
8	Pigs	quack
9	Hens	grunt
10	Ducks	squeak
11	Frogs	neigh
12	Mice	croak

d Write the sentences that are true.

1 Sara and Paul went to a farm.
Sara and Paul went to a zoo.
2 They saw no animals.
They saw lots of animals.
3 There were no monkeys in the zoo.
There were monkeys in the zoo.
4 The snakes were in the reptile house.
The snakes were in the monkey house.
5 The children saw an old horse.
The children saw a young giraffe.

e Add a letter to each of the words below to make the name of an animal. Choose letters from those in the box.

m	s	w	r	g

at   oat   nail   easel   ink

31

How much can you remember?

Write these sentences, putting in capital letters and full stops in the right places.

1 sara and paul go to school together
2 they meet mark and julie on the way
3 sara and julie are writing a story
4 sometimes the children go to the park

Write these sentences, choosing the right words from those in brackets.

5 The tables (is, are) in the hall.
6 The carpet (is, are) on the floor.
7 George reads (is, his) book.
8 Andy (is, his) drawing a picture.
9 I think (there, their) are two ponds in the park.
10 The children are eating (there, their) dinner.
11 Sara and Paul went (to, two) the zoo.
12 They saw (to, two) giraffes there.
13 Sara (as, has) a bicycle.
14 They went (as, has) soon (as, has) they were ready.
15 They walked to the corner (where, were) they met their friends.
16 The ducks (where, were) on the pond.

Write out and finish these.

17 We say one dog but two_____
18 We say one bun but two_____
19 We say one tin but two_____
20 We say one coat but two_____

32